RUSTAM SINGH

(b 1955), who writes poetry under the name Rustam, has published nine collections of poems in Hindi and a volume of his selected poems (2021). He has also published four books in English, under the name Rustam Singh, including *Literature, Philosophy, Political Theory: Selected Essays* (2022). He has translated into Hindi selected poems of Norwegian poets Olav Hauge (2008) and Lars Amund Vaage (2014). He has also translated into Hindi an anthology of poems of seven Panjabi poets (2022) and (with Teji Grover) selected poems of the Estonian poet Doris Kareva (2022). In addition, he has translated five other books into Hindi. Further, he has edited an anthology of eighteen contemporary Hindi poets (2025). He has held various research and editorial positions including the following: assistant editor of *Economic and Political Weekly*, Bombay; research associate at Centre for the Study of Developing Societies, Delhi; fellow at Indian Institute of Advanced Study, Shimla; editor of *Summerhill IIAS Review*, Shimla; founding editor of *Hindi: Language, Discourse, Writing*, New Delhi/Wardha; visiting scholar at Jawaharlal Nehru University, New Delhi; and senior fellow and senior editor at Eklavya Foundation, Bhopal. Before all this, he was a Captain in the Indian army.

rustamsingh1@gmail.com

Rustam is a poet with a rare wavelength. His calm, clear and concise sentences create an atmosphere of slightly eerie intensity. Like a captain of the crew, he spends no time on emotions. His visions tempt one to look over the edge, into the depth of nothingness, thrilled and trembling, sensing distant echoes of Beckett or Chirico.

Doris Kareva, *well-known European and Estonian poet*

Rustam is a rare poet of our times. He is among those few poets whose poetry is neither an imitation of the external world nor merely an impression of the inner. There are scenes, objects and materiality in his work, yet it seems as if there is something extra, something unreal. All the words, sentence combinations, everything, despite being familiar, creates something mysterious and supernatural. These poems demand solitary meditation from us, because their structure and beauty are extraordinary. Often rich in soft rhythm and inner heat, these poems are like an unlikely event in contemporary Hindi poetry.

Arun Kamal, *senior Hindi poet*

There comes a stage in literary pursuit when words start melting, meaning is no longer desired, it takes some other shape. Experiences that are inaccessible to words start taking form. The poet, Rustam, has been walking on this path. The distance between reality and perception has vanished in these poems. Standing between being and not being the poet is just watching.

Arun Dev, *poet and editor of Samalochan*

Rustam

The Rock Was Turning into Fire

Selected Poems {1985-2025}

translated from the Hindi by

Teji Grover & Rustam

RED RIVER

First published in May 2026 by
RED RIVER
157/1, Patparganj, New Delhi 110091
House No 9, Gyan Tirtha Path, Lankeshwar, Guwahati 781014

ISBN 978-81-69092-47-0

Edited and designed by Dibyajyoti Sarma
Typeset in IM FELL DW Pica 11 pt
Artworks used in the book, including the cover, are by Rustam Singh
Photographs are courtesy of the author
The handwritten texts in Hindi are by the author

Printed and bound in India by
The Book and Box Company,
(A Unit Of Ashwin Printing Agency),
40, Peters Road, Royapettah, Chennai 14

Price INR 399

Most typefaces used by 17th century English printers were of Dutch origin. The lack of material inspired Bishop of Oxford Doctor John Fell to purchase punches and matrices from Holland c 1670-1672 for use by the Oxford University Press. The so-named Fell types, presumed to be the work of Dutch punchcutter Dirck Voskens, mark a noticeable jump from previous designs, with considerably shorter extenders, higher stroke contrast, narrowing of round letters, and flattened serifs on the baseline and descenders. This book has been typeset in the open-source digitisation of the Fell Types released by designer and engineer Igino Marini

In memory of my father, mother and sister:
Shri Desa Singh Chauhan, Ms Kirpal Kaur
and Ms Sarabjeet Kaur,

and for Teji Grover

Preface: **The Transcendence of the Anthropomorphic**
Madan Soni

These poems by Rustam are the poems of a man who is deeply troubled with the insurmountable reality of human life, a man who has struggled against and has finally become disenchanted with this reality. As he says in one of his poems, this is a reality which gods have long since abandoned — disappointed that they created this reality and crying at the state of the human world.

And since this reality includes the existence of this poet and his identity, at the peak of this disenchantment and struggle, these are ultimately poems about disenchantment with oneself — with being human — and fighting against oneself. The poet is reduced to a mere name or has forgotten his name; his self has abandoned him and gone somewhere else. This loss of the self is the ultimate source of the beauty and ethics of these poems. And therein lies the authenticity of this disenchantment and struggle. The poems are devoid of morality. Even if there is a human being in them, he/she is a 'non-human'. In the name of civilisation, there are desolation and ruins: rough lanes, broken roads, swaying buildings, collapsed houses, closed doors and windows.

In these poems the transcendence of the anthropomorphic, the detachment with it, in its inversion, comes across as the ultimate attachment with nature — something like the poet's identification with nature as the embodiment of his desire or the dream to be transformed into nature itself or into a part of it. It is not without reason that these poems are full of the objects called nature: the mountain, the desert, the river, the sea, the sky, the soil, the wind, the fire, and trees, bushes, leaves, rocks, stones, pebbles, water, rain, autumn, the owl, the crow, the eagle, the bat, the snake, and so on. And these objects often pulsate with life. And yet, through these very objects the poems repeatedly invoke the non-being, the death. They give space to graves and the dead, observe the life of the dead, witness the beauty of death, even long for it and open the natural door to it.

There are some poems that one might be tempted to call love poems (and some are poems of passion), but the expression of this love is often abstract, invisible, almost absent. There is not so much of love in them as there is of memory or longing. In these poems there is a translucent, visionary tranquility, on the other side of which the ever-echoing melancholy shimmers.

It is natural that their alienation and the struggle with reality results in a kind of surrealism, dreaming and fantasy. But these three things emerge as a reflection of the reality in the paradigm of these poems, as a kind of counterfactual or a counterpoint. The residual traces of reality keep their own reality ambivalent.

Madan Soni is a prominent Hindi critic.

Contents

Preface: The Transcendence of the Anthropomorphic
by Madan Soni 11

In the Blue Street 17 The Wind Comes and Leaves 18 The Rock 19
Inside the Brown Rock 20 Restless Life in Imagination 21
In the Mirror You're Not 22 The Sun 23 Images 24 Cemetery 25
Ancestors 26 Scents 27 The Shadow 28 Tonight 29 Evening 1 30
I Have to Think with Great Patience 31 Fear 1 32 Today Again 34 Blue
35 The River 3 36 The River 4 37 The Tree Was Blue 38
On a Leaf Alone 39 The Day Was Red or Green 40
Leaves of the Neem 41 The Crow Was Sad 42 The Sea 2 43
The Sea 3 44 The Sea 4 45 Let the Stones Lie Around 46
And Now There Were Too Many of Us 47 Night 1 48 Night 2 49
I'll not Miss That House 51 Prophet 52
By the Staircase in an Office-porch 53 It's Neither Night Nor Day 54
Whatever I Hated 55 Life, Life 56 It Was Nine in the Evening 57
In a Village in Spain, 2016 58 The House 59
Everything Has Changed 61 If We Go Very Deep, Very Deep Down 62
We Walked for a Long Time 63 The Water Was Not Water 64
Of Late 65 Stockholm Is Cold 66 Another Tiger Has Fallen 67
We Made Our Way into the Forest 68 I Walk 69 Sixteen Bullets 70
In That Land 71 The Door Was Open 72 There Was a River 73
Rajasthan 3 74 Rajasthan 9 75 That Winter 76
A Rock Was Standing in My Way 77 The First Time We Met 78
We Are Back to the Place 79 You Remember the Day 80
There Is a Blue Rock in the Distance 81
The Day the Animals Get Even with You 82
When I Was Roaming Around 84 Those Eyes Surround Me 85
A Flame 86 One by One They Left 87
Every Evening the Dogs Waited 88 There Is a Grave Far Away 80

Houses Are Stuck to Other Houses 90 A Scream 91
On the Empty Road 92 You've Gone to Bed 93
When for the Last Time We Parted 94 I Went into the Land of Stones 95
I Saw Her Who Did Not Exist 96 In the Evening Fog 97 At Night 98
We Four Animals 99 Hear Me in the Dark 100 Rose. Rose. 101
You Are Shining Blue 102 One Day She Will Return 103
We Came Out of Emptiness 104 The Abyss Came to Me 105
Rustam (Singh) is Destroyed 106 The Sun Was the Sun 107
It's Night 109 This Narrow Path 110 The Light is Disappearing 111
Black-brown Earth 112 So Many Paths 113 At the Turn of the Street 114
Yesterday Evening 115 What Returned 116
A Man Went Away Screaming 117 He Was Walking 118
We Will Go There 119 Come Tomorrow Again 120 I Will Dream 121
In the Pitch Darkness 122 Yesterday I Lost My Way 123 Green 2 124
All the Lights Will Be Off 125 So Many People Leave 126
Soon a Path 127 So Many Mirrors 128 My Memory 129
There Was a Fragrance 130 Red 7 131 Red 8 132 Red 10 133 Red 14 134
There Was Nothing Beyond that Point 135
So Many Centuries Had Passed 136 I Went Down into the Valley 137
Passing through Rocks and Stones 138 I Have Almost Forgotten You 139
I Was Walking Around 140 Whether I Come or I Do Not 141
I Knelt Down 142 The Dust on Which 143 Today 144
Slowly I Left Them All 145 One Step at a Time 146 Soon I Will 147
We Will Not Return 148

A Poet Is Born As a Poet
Rustam in conversation with Punjabi poet Gurpreet 151

The Rock Was Turning into Fire

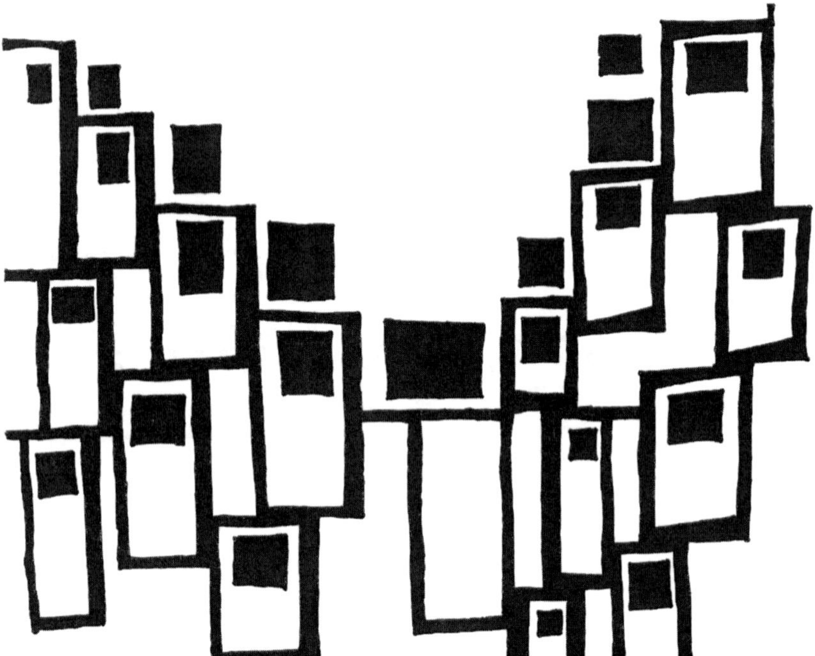

In the Blue Street

In the blue street
between the blue trees
the moon
walks with us.

Blue happy are your eyes.
On the blue lips dark is the smile.

A door is opening.
A song melts in the blue air.

In the ears
the rhythm sounds blue.

The Wind Comes and Leaves

The wind
comes and leaves
where doors could have been

The sun
blazes constantly
where
your laughter resounds

In this house
– which is not –
my memory is just my imagination

The Rock

The rock
was turning into fire
which was already fire and
looked like rock
among many other rocks
which were already fire and
looked like rocks   in a way that
among many fire-like rocks
at many a place
rock-like fire
was burning

Inside the Brown Rock

Inside the brown rock
inside the brown red rock
inside the red green rock
inside the green blue rock
brown red green blue
yellow sun was
fashioning itself
in which there was a
thousand-coloured rock
which in the beginning
appeared to be only brown
and had stung me

Restless Life in Imagination

Discontent
the rose
grows
without the memories of past lives

In the transparent mirror,
the transparent tear
is held up
on the edge of the transparent eye

The shadow
looks at its own shadow

Is almost real

Almost
alive

In the Mirror You're Not

In the mirror you're not

the mirror
in my imagination.

Black leaf
green flower
a drop of snow on blood
eyes that are clear and stone, a thing
                                        out of
                                        this world.

Then eyes that are clear and stone, a thing
                                        out of
                                        this world
                                        and within it

the mirror
that's now blank
                    and pure.

The Sun

The sun
is a string of lights
in the ray of death

How many moons
will just fall off
from the night sky?

You'll step on the bridge
I have made from
water

From the edge of a dream
I'll watch

Images

Images
tire even of me
and
of being images.

Surely
their patience has a limit
            for this insolent stranger

Surely
they dream
of another world
in which they are suffixes

Then
they dream
of not being suffixes
                        either

Cemetery

At times a poem
gets stuck in the pores of a heel.

What walks to the cemetery
is the automatism of words.

What sits there and weeps
is the fatigue of letters –

with no desire to return.

Ancestors

A point comes
where the words
turn only one way

Another point comes
and they lose the
desire to go on

Here they sit
and commune with their
ancestors

Scents

The tendency of some scents to have been just now somewhere here, around, inheres probably in their fragility. And this fragility in their desire to be a scent. And what should I say of this desire? In the context of a particular scent it was just now here, and is no longer here.

Some scents refuse to be captured in the mesh. Some are purely mirrors beyond oblivion. Some live in the dream. Some dream. There are some scents which knock at a door, in another mirror, somewhere

when we say:

he must have passed this way, here, and then here

this is his unwashed shirt

the wind
blew this way, then that

The Shadow

The shadow
knows me
Do I
know the shadow

In the mirror
which is only a mirror
the shadow is the light

In the eyes
which are not just the eyes
the shadow is a mystery

Tonight

Tonight
I will think of my father.
He was good to look at
and full of valour.
Tranquil and wrathful,
he was rich in swordsmanship.
To put up, quietly, with grief
we had learnt from him
and always to support what is just.
Finally, it was injustice and grief
which put an end to him:
He could not bear the absence of my mother
and the banality of our times.

Evening 1

A flower
just happened to be in my room.

It was evening, and a flower
had just stepped into my room.

It had to
touch my senses.

Yes, that evening,
a flower was to
bend over my navel.

In the fading light,
its tongue was
about to
sting my
navel.

I Have to Think with Great Patience

I have to think with great patience
about the fact that you are nowhere,
the fact that you will not turn up.

You are not there, you will not visit me –
I have to let this knowledge simmer in the pot
with great patience,
I have to let it turn into a nectar I can savour.

Then I have to
let the nectar
settle into my soul,
slowly,
with great patience.

Fear 1

I live in fear,
fear
sticks to me.

My soul
trembles
like an
everyday thing.

I step out,
then
step back in.

I think of fear,
write about it:

there is fear, too,
on the paper
here.

Words
leap up at me,
frighten me:

how
twisted
their face is!

Thought is fear
Meaning is fear
Speech is fear
Voice is fear

Love is fear
The beloved is fear
The body is fear
Breath is fear

Today Again

Today again
I chanced upon my mother and father.
They tottered on the road,
father in front, mother behind;
they were much older.
In the hot sun
their steps
swayed.
Where were they coming from?
Father held a stick,
his white clothes were dirty, torn.
Tied to the bag on mother's heavy shoulder,
empty, without a lid trundled a green plastic
bottle.
Then father
raised his head
and peered at the other side of the road.
What did he see when there was nothing there?
Mother
stood beside him.
She too stared at the same spot.
Then,
dodging the traffic,
they crossed the road.

Blue

The days were all blue. None was magnificent. I would imagine one of them as magnificent. Even so, it would continue to be blue. Blue was only a colour; it could well have been red, brown or yellow, too. Whatever the colour, the day looked just the same. That is, blue or red or brown or yellow, but just the same. This way all the days were blue or red or brown or yellow.

One blue was blue, one green. One blue appeared to be green, but was actually blue. There was a blue that descended into my soul, like an infinite blue. One blue would master the pretence of being blue. It was clear that it wasn't blue, nor a colour other than blue. Only its pretence was blue.

Pretence could never stay blue for long. Ultimately pretence had no colour, although blue came close to being its colour. But this was true even of red, brown or yellow. Pretence would stay blue only so long as it could stay red, brown or yellow, too. This was the only relation between pretence and colour.

Something like a relation was there between colour and the mirror too. However, to call it a relation was to colour it in a colour – colour which was definitely blue. To think of colour and the mirror was to think only of blue. Every mirror had an infinite blue, which lived in the body of the mirror in such a way that when I looked at blue, I only saw the mirror.

The River 3

The empty river flowed. Every day with an empty mind, we sat on its bank. We do not know if the river liked our sitting there this way.

The hills seemed filled up with earth and rocks. The birds rippled in the air like empty bones. At times they swooped down into the river. They pretended to catch fish, over and over.

The fish drifted into their mouths exactly like fish.

The empty river flowed.

The River 4

I went to the river.
Today again I went to the river.
Like half a river, it was there.

Today again I went to the river.

The river
lay stretched out
in the sun;
today again when I went to the river.

What was the river thinking
stretched out in the sun?
What exactly was it thinking
when I went to the river?

The sun was falling over it.
Oh, what a sight it was!
The sun was
falling over the river.

A seemingly indolent
body of the river
lay there
inert;
today again, when I went to the river.

The Tree Was Blue

The tree
was blue,
then green,
then black.

Even as I
looked at it,

it went on
changing
its colours.

On a Leaf Alone

On a leaf alone
the light fell.
A leaf alone was green.
A leaf alone shook,
slowly shook.
The earth was quiet.
All of the earth was quiet.
A leaf alone shook.

The Day Was Red or Green

The day was red or green,
it was hard to tell.
I walked
on a red-red path.
A green leaf lay on it
whose veins were red.

Leaves of the Neem

Leaves of the neem were shedding over me.
The wind blew.
In the night-sky
the moon was about to ascend.
I was sitting under the neem.
Green and yellow
leaves of the neem were shedding over me.

The Crow Was Sad

The crow was sad.

Sad. Sad.

The crow was sad.

I don't know why he was sad, but sad he was. I had seen in his eyes a feeling of despair. There is no doubt that he was sad. At times anger lit up his face, but then he would soon be sad again. He glanced with an eagle-eye at a fledgling sparrow or cracked open the sparrow's eggs and slurped them up, but would continue to be sad. Even when he picked up a fight with other crows or sitting on the roof-edge he cawed, it was quite clear that he was sad. At times, like an arrow, he darted to the river. Or would sit quietly for a while on a tree. Then with the same feeling of sadness, he would fly away and disappear for hours.

The Sea 2

The sea was everywhere. It encircled you. A wall that spread – you couldn't cross it.

The sea didn't leave you alone. Nor the wind that it sent. The wind penetrated your soul. You shivered, then shivered again.

The sea was always somewhere near. Then it came closer. Its sting was about to touch you and destroy you. You wished to be destroyed, didn't you? That's why you loved the sea.

But the sea was crafty. It changed its shapes, forms and colours. You were caught in its net. You couldn't see its cunning smile. You only saw countless dreams in the mirror. The sea took you into the mirror. Perhaps the sea itself was a mirror in that mirror. Or in some other mirror.

The Sea 3

There was a day when the sea was nothing. You touched it and it turned into the sea. Another day you touched it again. It burst into flames. On your fingers there was the imprint of touching it. Then you touched that imprint too. With that touch, the sea moved into your fingers.

The Sea 4

Blue fire arose from your fingers. But I knew it was the sea burning with the touch of your skin.

And the skin was cold. No, it wasn't blue. It was white like snow.

You had imprisoned the sea and it was smouldering in your cold icy skin.

Let the Stones Lie Around

Let the stones lie around.

They haven't learnt how to move.

To keep lying around somewhere –
this, too, is the way to live.

For years I have seen them
lying at this same spot.

And Now There Were Too Many of Us

And now there were too many of us.
And even the stones would shrink when they saw us.

Or we were very cruel,
very.

And we no longer recognised ourselves.

That's why I wished to stay with stones alone.

Actually, I wished to turn myself into a stone.

And O that I were a blue rock! A blue rock!
(This is how I would think.)

Or a mirror lying out somewhere.

Night 1

This is night.
Yes, night.
And this is me.
At this hour both of us are here.
Night is touching me, and I feel the night, but the night doesn't feel me. This way I can keep sitting here, just the way I am. And the night will continue to be what it is. Both of us know it, the night and I: I will keep feeling it, and it will remain the night. There is nothing it would want from me, or I from it.

Night 2

Night night night.
I want night, yes, the night.

And all these others, who among them doesn't want the night? Who? Everyone wants the night. Everyone wants the night because it is day here. And the day turns up again and again. That's why everyone wants the night. Day turns up again and again. Day day day. Day after day. Day, and then day again. Day turns up again and again, keeps on turning up. That's why everyone wants the night.

Day day day. Night night night.

Day day day. Day, even in night. I don't want the day, don't want it. Don't want the day at day, nor day at night. Not in anything, not even in a thing. Day day day. I don't want the day, don't want it.

I want only night, only night. And even in the day I want night.

And I want that even the day should be dark – dense, black – as night. Dense and black. Pitch dark. So that even the day feels like night. Like night, or night itself. It should feel as if I'm only in the night, am sitting in the night, even if it is day.

Day day day.

And it's true. I say it again. Certainly, I don't want the day. I have no doubt about that. I say it again and again, am ready to say it. Again and again, again and again. Again and again, how many times? As many times as it needs to be said. Am ready to say it. Here. There. Inside. Outside. Am ready to say it. Yes, I'm ready to renounce the day, be rid of it. Yes, I'm ready. I don't want it, don't want it. And in the night, I don't want the day at all. Yes, in the black night. Not even in sleep. Not even in dream. Day turns up. Keeps on turning up. But in night I don't want the day at all.

It's true. And I say it again.

But it's possible. And I say it in grief, that perhaps I don't want even the night, the way I don't want the day, don't want it. Perhaps now I neither want the day at day, nor night at night. Neither night at day, nor day at night. I say it in grief. Yes, I scream. That perhaps I don't want night and day, both day and night, don't want them. I say it in grief. Yes, I scream. Clench my fists. That day forces itself into night, makes a hole in it. Night takes fright, doesn't remain night. What a tragedy it is. What a tragedy. That day turns up in sleep, and then even in dream. That's why perhaps I don't want even the night, the way I don't want the day, don't want it. And I say it in grief. Yes, I scream. Clench my fists. What a tragedy it is. What a tragedy.

Where do I go now?

I'll Not Miss That House

I will not miss that house.
I will not miss that river.
I will not miss that forest.

I will forget about that town.

I will not miss those roads.
I will not miss those streets.

By missing something
what do you get?

What?

I will wipe away my memory.
I will make it

clean like a slate.

I will forget about everything.

Prophet

They didn't want me
to open my mouth.

They wanted that
they should speak
but not I.

In that garrulous age,
all they desired was to tell me their own thing.

They called me a prophet
and then threw me into a dark cell.

They pushed me into a blind well
because my voice was unnerving
and I spoke
only the truth.

Slowly
they sewed my lips.

By the Staircase in an Office-porch

By the staircase in an office-porch
that good animal stood.
Surely, he wasn't well
and was rotting from the inside –
the porch was stinking of decay.
He was quiet, almost still, but his eyes
bore an invisible pain,
intense and throbbing
and which
I had sensed.
It wasn't obvious how long he would suffer this pain,
when he would meet his end,
when he would crumble and fall.

For years I had stifled the thought,
but that was the day
when for the first time
I cursed Nature
that had begotten Life.

It's Neither Night Nor Day

It's neither night
nor day.
Or let's say,
both night and day are here,
broken
into pieces –

This strange scene
that I'm watching –
or I'm inside it –
is
it
a painting
in which
night and day lie scattered
in a disorderly fashion
and are torn,
cut,
are stuck together again,
have taken a zigzag turn,
are fed up with themselves,
are bored with their life,
have lost their way?

Night and day
are both broken.
Or let's say,
it's neither night nor day.

Whatever I Hated

Whatever I hated,
you loved –

we desired,
we despaired,
we Lived.

Then one day
Life came to an end.

Just the rocks, the stones, the dust.
And mountains. And snow.
And the lava rising.

The earth
turned to its source.
A wandering ball of fire.

It exploded in the sky.

Then the sky, too, was gone.

Life, Life

Life, life,
this is what you did.

This cup of blood
all the time I have drunk.
This mutilated heart.
Whoever gave it to me?
Who?

O Satan!
You inhabit my being!
You flow in my veins!

And I,
this frail creature,
dance to your tune!

Look here!
I'm flinging you back
into the void
from where you came!

Get lost!
And don't show up again!

It Was Nine in the Evening

It was nine in the evening.
The city was blazing with lights.
Cars came and went,
cars honking away, cars screeching to a halt.
The roads were full of smoke.
And I saw that
bang in the midst of this tumult
at the crossing
a lone animal stood.

In the uncouth
human-world
a terror-stricken animal
in whose eyes
every now and then
lights went piercing by –

not a trace of
radiance
in those eyes!

In a Village in Spain, 2016

Two people getting old
sat on chairs
in the tiny lawn of the house.
I didn't think they were talking,
nor were they reading.
They just sat there
facing the sun
in the west,
warmed themselves in the soft, sweet, rare sun of winter.

Looking at them, I could tell they had known each other for a long time.

Sitting there they didn't seem out of place. In fact, it looked as if they were familiar with every corner of that house. Knew well the good and bad habits of each other and put up with them.

Even so they struck me as two frail statues
which could collapse any moment.
Their carefully well-kept house could fall anytime.
Their world
could disappear
without a murmur.

The House

1

The house stands the way it must have stood here years ago.
The windows are open. The sun is streaming in.
Things are lying about wherever they did.

Almirahs, books, shelves. Other things, too.

In a corner of the front room two chairs.
An old person sits in one of them, the other is vacant.

No one will turn up, it seems.

2

In the rundown house someone coughs.
A cat goes round and round, round and round in the courtyard.
On a ramshackle cot an ancient woman sits –
grimy clothes, unkempt hair, eyes waiting for someone.

Who had gone away? Who is to come or will never come?

3

Once there was a house here.

A cat still comes:
she jumps from the roof to the ledge.

The crow laughs almost endlessly.
The doors open and then shut.

The leaves whirl.

The wind
wanders about in the house
that once was here.

Everything Has Changed

Everything has changed.
Or, I have forgotten.
When did we come here?
When did we pass through this place?
Everything is different
and dead.

The hills are still there
but they are bare:
just the rocks and stones.

The sun still rises.

A pit
spews out lava.

A pebble glitters.

The three trees have disappeared.

A horse
that had galloped away
is just a thought.

The thought is beautiful.

If We Go Very Deep, Very Deep Down

If we go very deep, very deep down,
if we don't stop by the shrub that has a single flower,
if we don't look up at the blue hill on the other side,
but just keep going down to where the river is,
with very little water, almost empty,
if we sit down and keep sitting right there,
deep down, at the riverbank, and don't say a word,
only listen to the sounds, just listen....

We Walked for a Long Time

We walked for a long time
and stopped
in an alien province.
No one knew us.
We were alone in that crowd
like the tree in the desert we had passed by
on which
an old crow was cawing –

and every moment
our life was in danger.

Do you remember
why we had left
turning our back to home and hearth?
Because the rivers had dried up
and the land gone barren;
one by one the animals had died,
and friends had begun to avert their eyes.

And it was for the first time
that we saw gods laughing –
perhaps they were happy
that the fair was winding up
and they'd soon be free.

The Water Was Not Water

The water was not water, the air was not air, the rivers were not rivers, the lakes were not lakes, the sea was not the sea, the clouds were not clouds, love was not love, God was not God.

I was born into such a world, I lived there and then left.

Of Late

Of late, some strange scenes I have come across:

A mirror was flying in the storm.
A door was drifting in the flood.
A tree collapsed suddenly.
A bird
couldn't use its
wings.

Wherever I went an injured animal groaned – its wounds couldn't be healed, it was so deeply hurt.

I'm God, I'm God, a mad person shouted, I'm the one who made this hell.

All over the earth there were patches of blood that were red here, and there green.

Stockholm Is Cold

Stockholm is cold.
The sea here is broken into pieces.
The ships look like boats.
The wind stings like an arrow.
But your body
tries to warm up my
dead soul.

A tall man has come out of the ancient past. He has grey hair and beard. And on his face is frozen the same old stubborn smile.

My face has aged somewhat, a bald woman says.

'Things here are poisoned. That's why I live away from the city.'

'Everyone is just as they were. But I have changed. Now I walk with a limp.'

Iron steps
are sliding down
into the abyss.

The earth is returning
to its womb.

Another Tiger Has Fallen

Another tiger has fallen.
Another elephant has died.
Another leopard has
lost
to
you.

I, too,
in your crowd

a long time ago

was surrounded
just like them.

You were armed with
rods, swords
and who knows what else.

We Made Our Way into the Forest

We made our way into the forest.
As usual,
it was mushrooms we wanted to pick.
But that day
they were acting strangely.
From a distance we could see them,
but when we came closer, they would disappear.
We couldn't pick a single mushroom.
We ventured deeper into the forest,
not meaning to fell trees,
but the trees were afraid of us.
Wherever we went,
they would slide to another place.
We kept wandering in the forest;
often we lost our way.
Finally, we turned back to leave.
But the trees laid siege to us,
they had huddled together –
there was no way we could escape.

Seasons came and left.
We don't know how long we stood there.
What could we do? Where could we go?
We turned into trees.

I Walk

I walk
and the street begins to sink.
It appears as if I'm stepping into a cavern.
Buses and cars leap up at me.
Buildings shake and stagger.
Every face laughs a demonic laugh.
From a distance I see someone familiar,
when he comes near, he turns into a stranger.
How many people here walk without feet
and speak without a tongue,
in a language I have never heard!
On the roads, in the streets, in homes and houses,
all the time I hear someone weeping.

Sixteen Bullets

based on an actual incident

Sixteen bullets
they fired
at the elephant that was me.
I had managed to escape from the circus
after ten years of bondage.
I was in a city.
I had no idea where to go. I only wanted to escape.
The police and a crowd followed me.
They wanted to catch me again.
I went on a rampage.
I ran.
Sixteen bullets were fired at me,
one by one.
I was bewildered,
my eyes wide open with fear.
Why was I
being killed?
All I wanted was to be free.

In That Land

In that land
wherever we set foot
the earth cracked.
The sky fell upon us.
The wind blew us away –
it hurled us just anywhere.
The water drowned us.
The fire burnt us.
No one visited our graves –
slowly they too disappeared.

The Door Was Open

The door was open.
She came into the house,
picked up my photo and kept looking at it.
Sat on the chair on which I used to sit.
Kept thumbing through my books.
At times a smile danced on her lips.
Through the window the sun was falling on her hair.
Then she picked up one of my shirts, smelled it,
held it close to her chest for a long time, and left.

There Was a River

There was a river I have almost forgotten.
Some rocks, lying out somewhere.
Shores of the sea,
sand and some stones – the water drenched them, then left.
Somewhere there a woman was picking up pebbles.
Behind her, a vast body of water,
over which, at places, white light shimmered in the sun.
Who were we? Why were we there? Now I don't remember.

Rajasthan 3

We left early in the morning.
We loaded our stuff on bullock-carts,
abandoned our houses and stepped out.
That was the only way to escape that barren land.
We moved towards the north-west.
We had heard, that was where the land was still green.
In the scorching heat of the afternoon sun, we saw a tree.
It had no shade.
Not a single bird was sitting on it.
There were skeletons of animals wherever we went.
Vultures had eaten them and left.
In the evening, outside a town,
dogs were fighting over some bones.
They themselves were little more than bones.
The town was almost empty.
It was during one such evening that they surrounded us.

Rajasthan 9

It was a magical land.
The further we went the more distant
we became from the place we had to reach.
Yet, at every moment it seemed so near.
Even in dust it glittered like glass.
At night we would hear sounds of bells.
Close to our tents strange lights shimmered.
We noticed that we were surrounded
by shadows before which our weapons were useless.
We were not scared,
but then one day we just turned back before reaching anywhere.

That Winter

That winter of 1870, how cold it was!
And that spring of 1980!

He had fixed his gaze on your body.
You had unearthed the spring of youth.

Ah! How dazzling it was, the street
that Monet had painted in Sainte-Adresse!
A white butterfly flew around.
And a heart was singing.

The moon's milk
was dripping on to the earth.

And that nymph stood naked in front of St Anthony.

To tempt you I had spread out my legs!
But how heavy was the weight of your thighs!

Before that phantom house,
Saturn was eating its own child.
I was looking into the mirror, or the mirror into me?

A Rock Was Standing in My Way

A rock was standing in my way.
Brown red blue and yellow,
a rock was standing in my way.
I stopped walking, I just stayed there
because a rock was standing on my path that day.
What else could I do? I looked at it
because a rock was standing in my way.
It stood still. It did not move.
And how it glittered in the sun!
A thousand rays of colour
were bursting out of it!
Had it blocked my path?
Had it snatched from me
my desire to keep on walking –
brown red blue and yellow
the rock that was standing in my way?
I do not know. I do not know.
All I remember is
a rock was standing in my way.

The First Time We Met

The first time we met,
you knocked on the door,
I opened it.
On your face I could see
longing, hesitation, fear and many other things.
I asked you to come in, take a chair.
I didn't know you and why you had come.
Facing each other we sipped our tea,
your knees were touching my knees.
Your gaze was fixed on my face,
I couldn't read what it was trying to say.
To tell you the truth, I too was a little scared,
inside me I trembled and shivered.
Thus, we kept sitting there until it was time for you to leave.

We Are Back to the Place

We are back to the place from where we started, though it has changed a lot. Do you think it recognises us? Our horses are tired. Our cheeks sunken. We are covered with dust. People who knew us, where are they? What coming back is this? Look! How like strangers we stand here!

But possibly the banyan
that stands in the distance
still remembers us.

And surely the stones
in that dried up river
wouldn't have forgotten us.

You Remember the Day

You remember the day
when the horses had surrounded the city?
Try to remember:
People were up, they were leaving for work,
when they saw horses on the borders of the city.
How many were they? It's hard to say.
All around the city,
up to the far distance,
there were only horses.
Slowly, they moved ahead. First, they blocked the roads.
Then they entered the streets, the colonies.
They pressed on.
They filled up every space in the city.
They were
so close together
and moving in such a way
it was impossible to stop them.
The day went by. It was noon. Then evening.
People crowded into houses, in shops and on rooftops.
When the sun was going down
everywhere in the city
one could see
only horses.
They neighed, they fluttered their nostrils, they shook their heads
and
stood huddled together
until it was dark.

There Is a Blue Rock in the Distance

There is a blue rock in the distance. Close to it glistens a body of water.

Look! Something is hiding behind it. Or it has stopped there for a moment. Or, maybe, it just belongs to that place.

If we wish, we can go there and take off its cover.

But we will not do that.

We have been wandering around here for a long time. By now we know every corner of this desert.

But we will not unravel this mystery. We will not violate its sovereign existence.

Let's turn back.

The Day the Animals Get Even with You

The day the animals get even with you,
what fun that will be!
Ha ha ha ha ha ha ha ha

When they turn you into slaves,
what fun that will be!
Ha ha ha ha ha ha ha ha

When they put you in cages,
what fun that will be!
Ha ha ha ha ha ha ha ha

When they slash your throats,
what fun that will be!
Ha ha ha ha ha ha ha ha

When they cook your flesh,
what fun that will be!
Ha ha ha ha ha ha ha ha

When they flay you from head to foot,
what fun that will be!
Ha ha ha ha ha ha ha ha

When they adorn themselves with your skin,
what fun that will be!
Ha ha ha ha ha ha ha ha

When they make medicines from your limbs,
what fun that will be!
Ha ha ha ha ha ha ha ha

When they make you dance in the circus,
what fun that will be!
Ha ha ha ha ha ha ha ha
Ha ha ha ha ha ha ha ha
Ha ha ha ha ha ha ha ha

When I Was Roaming Around

When I was roaming around
on desolate roads,
you were just ahead of me.
Then I found you close behind.
Your shadow was touching my heels
whereas you yourself were
just a shadow.
No, you were not a chimera
because I could clearly see
even the shadow of your shadow
just when I was roaming around
alone
on desolate roads.

Those Eyes Surround Me

Those eyes surround me.
Those eyes stare at me.
Those eyes follow me.

When we were in the desert
and a stone was on fire,
I said to you –
Look, those eyes are lying on the ground.
These are not eyes, you said,
it's a dead sparrow.
This is how all alone they die,
not a soul around them.

Then I saw
a tree
was loaded with eyes.
You said –
These are crows,
they are screaming.
A crow has just died.
They are mourning.

The Narmada had dried up.
When we were looking at it,
to me,
it appeared to be an eye.
You said –
It's a glittering band of sand
from here up to there.

A Flame

A flame was spreading along the wall, consuming it.
Blue, black and yellow that flame I had not seen before
nor the wall it consumed.
I lay down facing the wall when they came to kill me.

One by One They Left

One by one they left.
Yes, one by one they all left.
And I'm still here.
One by one they left.
Someone left all at once.
Someone did not wish to leave.
Someone was looking back again and again.
Someone suddenly collapsed.
Someone kept on leaving for a long time.
Someone wasn't being able to leave.
One by one they left,
they all left.
And I'm still here.

Every Evening the Dogs Waited

Every Evening the dogs waited at that deserted spot.
At a certain time two old people came, gave them food and left.
Then one day they didn't turn up.

There Is a Grave Far Away

There is a grave far away, alone, at a desolate place.
It's buried in mud and brambles.
A tree is bent over it, is about to fall.
The one who is lying in it
has long been forgotten.
No one will visit him.

Houses Are Stuck to Other Houses

Houses are stuck to other houses,
houses have climbed over other houses.
Houses are standing straight, houses are bent.
Houses are crooked, aslant, cut.
Some houses are at a distance, away from other houses.
Some are leaking, torn.
Some are houses only in name:
those who own them are actually houseless.

And I will not talk about the house of my mother and father.
No, I will not utter a word about it.
Not a word.

A Scream

A scream was rising from that pit.
I walked towards it, went up to its edge, looked into it.
There was nothing inside it.
But a scream was rising from that pit.

On the Empty Road

On the empty road I was walking alone.
She too was walking along with me.
It was neither day nor night nor evening,
nor light nor dark.
There was only the road on which I was walking alone.
She too was walking along with me.

I was neither alive nor dead
and this
was no journey at all.
I was not moving towards a destination.
On the empty road I was walking alone.
She too was walking along with me.

You've Gone to Bed

You've gone to bed.
In my room still lingers the fragrance of your self.
Outside in the kadamba tree,
owls are still flapping their wings.
A part of me says, everything should stop just as it is;
another says,
I'd love to see you in the morning
yet again.

When for the Last Time We Parted

When for the last time we parted at that desolate spot,
I left you there,
under the earth.
Then it struck me you might feel lonely lying utterly alone.
I dug another grave by your side and placed my heart in it.
Thus, I withdrew from that spot.
My heart now lay there with you.
I spent my remaining days on the earth without a heart.

I Went into the Land of Stones

I went into the land of stones.
A sensation shot through the air.
I smelt anger.
I saw hostility.
Why have you come here? I heard.
Many a stone encircled me.
Even so I went a little further.
Now I stood touching a rock,

when a heavy,
stony hand
hit me on the head.

When I woke up, I was lying on the edge of their land.

I Saw Her Who Did Not Exist

I saw her who did not exist.
She knew I was there.
She got up,
moved towards me –
she touched my cheeks.
She looked like a woman from some ancient times.
Come again tomorrow, she said.
I was standing at the bottom of an arid hill.
There was no one around.

In the Evening Fog

In the evening fog
I was walking alone
when I found myself
surrounded by the dead.
I wanted to go further
but I stopped there.
They stood around me,
silently,
just looked at me.
I could have walked on
but I too stood there,
looking at them,
just as they were looking at me,
and went on looking
in that fog
for a long time.

At Night

At night, I was sitting in front of the house
facing the street.
The dead were going somewhere carrying their coffins.
First one, then another, then there were many of them.
Slowly they turned into a crowd.
Their coffins were falling apart.
They themselves too were just bones.
When they walked their joints creaked.
At times one of them looked at me,
then walked on.
Leaving their cemeteries where were they going?
Were they looking for new graves?
Or was it some impending doom they were trying to escape?

We Four Animals

We four animals set out to hunt.
We had not eaten for many days.
Up to the far distance there were small hills.
In between them there were
green and dry bushes, thorns, leaves, some flowers.
We would climb a hill, look into the distance,
smell the air, then set off again.
We were getting weaker, losing speed.
Our bones began to show.
We four animals set out to hunt.
We had not eaten for many days.

Hear Me in the Dark

Hear me in the dark.
Come to me in the dark.
In the dark, we will twinkle like fireflies,
scream like bats,
fly like owls, flap our wings.
In the dark, our eyes will glow.
Curiously we will look at things
shining in the light of our eyes,
in a world
full of wonder
on the other side of the day.

Rose. Rose.

Rose. Rose.

Eyes are rose.
The breath is rose.
The armpits:
rose.

How like a rose your breasts open up and then shut down!
The nipples surge like roses, change colour!

The thighs are rose.
The legs are rose.
The navel is rose.

And from your rose-bush trickle fragrant juices of countless roses!
Rose. Rose.

You Are Shining Blue

You are shining blue
and black and yellow.
The blue is shining on your hips,
there's a brown line down the middle of them
that runs to a black hollow.
A bit of yellow is stuck on the blue-black thigh,
the ankle is white-blue.

One Day She Will Return

One day she will return.
She will step over the threshold into this house.

But she will find the house empty.

She will encounter here
only a memory.

We Came Out of Emptiness

'We came out of emptiness,
will disappear into emptiness,' you said,

whereas I could see
an emptiness right there between the two of us

and an emptiness
at the place
where my heart used to be,
a heart that was failing to touch you.

The thing that I faced,

was it you,

or was it

just an
emptiness?

The Abyss Came to Me

The abyss came to me.
It clutched me.
It pulled me into itself.
Now that's where I live.

Rustam (Singh) Is Destroyed

Rustam (Singh) is destroyed.
Rustam (Singh) is finished.
Rustam (Singh) is now only a name.
He has no mind.
He has no self.

Yesterday I saw him on the road.
There were cars, there was dust, there was smoke,
there was noise.
He staggered as he walked.
He didn't know which way he was going.

I began to follow him.

The Sun Was the Sun

The sun was the sun.
What was I in front of it?
The mountain was the mountain.
What was I in front of it?
The jungle was the jungle.
What was I in front of it?
The sea was the sea.
What was I in front of it?
The desert was the desert.
What was I in front of it?

The rock was the rock.
What was I in front of it?
The stone was the stone.
What was I in front of it?
The pebble was the pebble.
What was I in front of it?

A grain of sand
was a grain of sand.
What was I in front of it?

The wind was the wind.
What was I in front of it?
The water was the water.
What was I in front of it?
The fire was the fire.
What was I in front of it?
The dust was the dust.
What was I in front of it?

At the end
I drowned in the water,
the wind flew me away,
the fire burned me,
I got buried in the dust.

It's Night

It's night.
Between tall houses
in a narrow street

I'm walking.
Everything is black –
even the lights.

This Narrow Path

This narrow path will touch the black mountain
which at places looks like ash.
Then climbing over it,
it will cross the summit and go down on the other side.
There once again it will enter the wilderness.
I'll walk along with it
and will stop where it stops.

The Light Is Disappearing

The light is disappearing in the fog.
The darkness is growing.
Are they two or four who are walking just ahead of me?

Black-brown Earth

Black-brown earth was on both sides of it.
The meandering path
merged into
the lake
surrounded by red mountains.
Even in the lake I kept walking on that path.
In front of me the lake just parted.

So Many Paths

So many paths.
I walk on them and reach nowhere.
At every turn
from behind a tree
or a rock
death stares at me.

At the Turn of the Street

At the turn of the street suddenly you appeared.
We looked at each other.
Immediately I knew you were from some other world.
I began to follow you.

Yesterday Evening

Yesterday evening
when I was staggering along the road,
the whole scene staggered.

Just then
a tree broke
and fell to the ground.

What Returned

What returned
wasn't you
but your apparition.
I walked behind it,
followed it.
I called out your name.
It stopped and looked back at me.
I ran towards it,
tried to catch it.
My hand
went through to its other side.
Then it began to walk again.

A Man Went Away Screaming

A man went away screaming.
Another was so tired, he couldn't move.
There was also a third who was full of wounds.
A fourth was heartbroken.
There was a fifth one too.

He Was Walking

He was walking.
Then he collapsed.
And he gave up trying.
He did not wish to get up.
How long will I keep on walking?
He asked.
How much longer?

No one was listening.

We Will Go There

We will go there, to that desolation.
We will wander around.
I will stick a dry flower in your white hair.
You will throw a pebble into the sky;
it will not come back.
I will move a hill and make a path.
We will wait for it but this time there'll be no spring.

Come Tomorrow Again

Come tomorrow again.
Even in death we will keep meeting
in this park,
on this bench,
under these trees.

I Will Dream

I will dream.
And no, I will not dream.
On a long, narrow path I'll walk.
A stone will be lying in the middle of it.
There'll be a tree too embedded in it.
A horse will be standing around.
I will go past them.
I will hear the sound of laughter.
A crow will scream.
An eagle will pounce.
A vortex of dust will rise –
its crown
touching the sky.
A vortex of dust will rise.

In the Pitch Darkness

In the pitch darkness only the path was shining.
On both sides there were hills but they were not visible.
Everything stood still.
Neither the road was moving, nor I, nor the wind, nor the hills,

not even the darkness.

Yesterday I Lost My Way

Yesterday I lost my way.
I left the house
and began to walk.
I kept walking for a long time.
I forgot that I had to get back home.
I could see everything, yet nothing was visible,
as if I was passing through a fog.
Then I,
surrounded by that same fog,
sat down
on the side of the road.

Green 2

Once again
your eyes are turning green.
Or else
this is an illusion.
It's possible
they have never changed their colour.
Even then,
looking into them,
a flash of lightning
has shot through my veins.

All the Lights Will Be Off

All the lights will be off.
We will watch the sun going down.
The darkness will grow.
Things will turn into shadows.
The shadows will move,
will merge into one another.
What strange shapes they will form!
To someone else
we too will appear to be
a moving, changing shape.

So Many People Leave

Don't go.
Where will I look for you?

So many people leave.
Then they don't come back.

As if there are many worlds.
And the wall between them breaks down at a point.
And someone wanders to the other side
and can't find the gap in the wall to return.

Soon a Path

Soon
a path will emerge
in this barren land
and on it a silhouette
coming towards you.

So Many Mirrors

So many mirrors on the wall.

When I look into them I don't see any face.

My Memory

My memory is an old mirror.

Your image is getting blurred.

There Was a Fragrance

There was a fragrance
in that desolation.
I knew
you were somewhere around.

Red 7

You will come –
after how many centuries? –
under that deserted bridge.

You will find
many dry, red roses.

You will count them
and know
for how many days
I had waited for you.

Red 8

Crossing many cities and towns
he reached that place,
under that deserted bridge.

He picked up a dry, red rose,
smelled it
and stood holding it.

When last I saw him,
he was standing like a statue
holding the rose.

Red 10

Glancing one last time
at those white bones
and a red stone
in that thin river,
I left the place.

Red 14

I looked all over the city.
She was nowhere.

Not a single face looked like her face,
nor the body, the gait.

I left the city.

There was a red pebble on the road.

I bent down to pick it up.

There Was Nothing Beyond that Point

There was nothing beyond that point.
If we were to raise our feet, then which way?
If we were to put down our feet, then where?

Even the abyss was not there.

So Many Centuries Had Passed

So many centuries had passed.
I waited for you.
You came.
How much you had changed!
You looked at me as if I was a stranger.
A cold wave came towards me.
I shuddered.

I Went Down into the Valley

I went down into the valley.
There were rocks and stones.
There was dust.
There were scorpions and snakes.

There was no green
anywhere.

Just a dead tree standing there, alone.

Passing through Rocks and Stones

Passing through rocks and stones,
we will descend from the mountain
to the place where a river with a sharp current flows.
We will turn back
and kneel before the mountain with folded hands.
We will sit on the banks of the river for a long time,
watch it flow,
taste its water for the last time.
Then taking in the entire scene in our eyes,
we will jump into the water.

I Have Almost Forgotten You

I have almost forgotten you.
A faint shadow comes to my memory.
How long will I remember that too?

I Was Walking Around

I was walking around waiting for you
at that deserted place.
I moved a stone: a snake ran out from under it.
I saw a tree standing there alone, drying up.
There was a horse too somewhere in my thoughts;
he had wandered off.
I climbed a barren hill: a shrivelled brown flower lay on it.
I waited for you till the sun went down.
You did not come. I moved deeper into that wilderness.

Whether I Come or I Do Not

Whether I come or I do not,
you wait for me.
It's possible that I come.
It's possible that I don't come.
But you wait for me.
There are so many things that can stop me!
What am I but just a straw?
If a storm comes, I'll be hurled away to some other place.
If it rains, I will drown.
Who knows,
I may not be able even to cross the road.
But you wait for me.

I Knelt Down

I knelt down
and asked forgiveness from the earth.

I knelt down before a stone,
before a tree.

A plant was moving in the wind.
An animal passed by me.

A mountain was swaying.

The sea was surging towards the land.

I knelt down and asked forgiveness from them all.

The Dust on Which

The dust on which
I walked away from you
no longer has the imprints of my feet.

You too will disappear
from my memory
one day.

Then,
another day,
I'll forget myself too.

Today

Today, even the body is sad.
The bones are sad,
the flesh is sad.
Every cell of the body is filled with sadness.

Where are those whom I loved?
Those whom I touched are also so far away.

In front of me
there is a ruined city
in whose deserted streets
I'm roaming alone.

Slowly I Left Them All

Slowly I left them all.
Or they left on their own and did not come back.

Now in this haunted house,
like an old ghost,
in its crumbling rooms,

I roam day and night.

At times,
the sound of something breaking, of something falling

echoes through the house

and the echo keeps ringing in my ears for a long time.

One Step at a Time

One step at a time
I walked away from you
in that desolate space.
You had your back towards me.
You were looking at some point far away.

Soon I Will

Soon
I will turn you into a memory –

and then into oblivion.

We Will Not Return

We will not return.

Our backs will turn
toward this place.
Our feet will start moving.

Our eyes
will not look back.

एक क़ब्र है दूर उजाड़ में

एक क़ब्र है दूर उजाड़ में अकेली।
वह मिट्टी और झंखाड़ में दब गयी है।
एक वृक्ष उस पर झुका हुआ है, उस पर
गिरने को है।
जो इसमें पड़ा है
सब उसे भूल चुके हैं।
अब कोई उसे मिलने नहीं आयेगा।

वहाँ से भागकर

वहाँ से भागकर हम कहाँ जाते?
प्रलय वहाँ भी था, और वहाँ भी।
उस विनाशकारी समय में
हम जहाँ भी पाँव रखते थे,
धरती सरक जाती थी।

—रुस्तम

A Poet Is Born
As a Poet
Rustam in conversation with
Punjabi poet Gurpreet

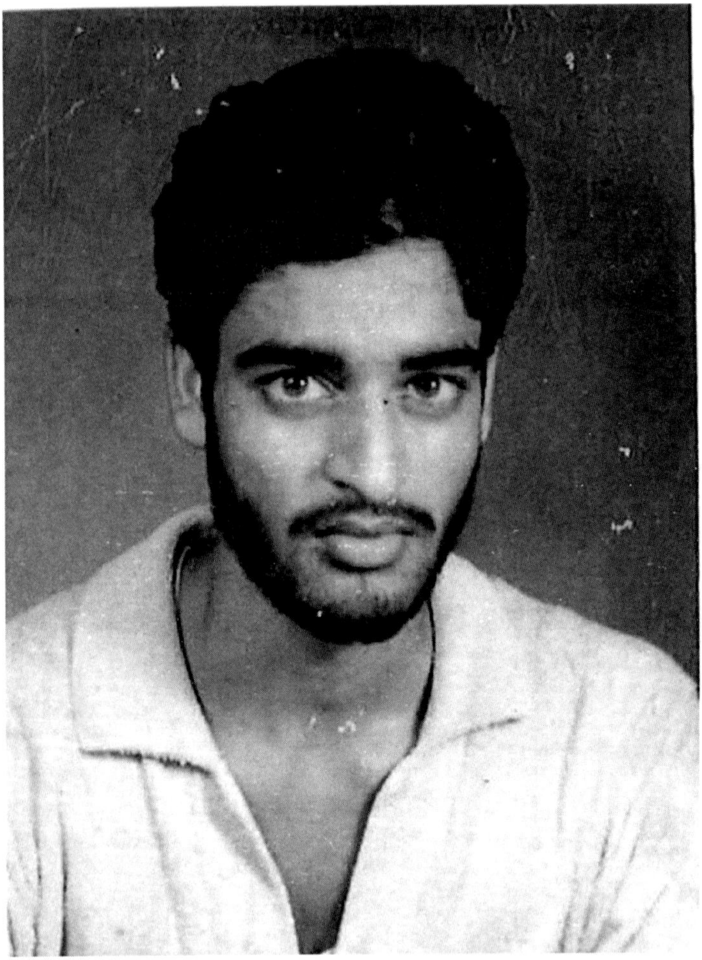

Rustam at 18

मेरी आत्मा काँपती है
रुस्तम

न तो मैं कुछ कह रहा था
रुस्तम

जो है और जैसा है
रुस्तम

क्योंकि मैं
फूल की छाया
में था
रुस्तम

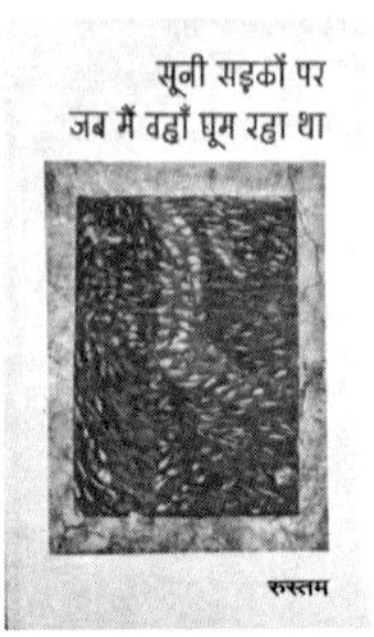

सूनी सड़कों पर
जब मैं वहाँ घूम रहा था
रुस्तम

मैं
पृथ्वी से
बिछुड़
गया था
रुस्तम

और काश कि मैं एक नीली शिला होता
चुनी हुई कविताएँ
1985-2020
रुस्तम

'I don't know why I read poetry and why I write it.' This statement of yours is very deep. The 'why' of writing is not simple and straightforward. But I tend to think it is always there. Did you never try to find it out? See if you can find it today.

Let's look at your question. I believe that a poet is born as a poet. That is, the desire to write poetry is innate. When we are born, this desire is already there in us. As we grow up, this desire within us begins to prompt us, telling us to write poetry. The appropriate word for this desire is instinct. We can also call it a drive. In other words, we are possessed by this desire, this instinct, and we have to do what it wants. We can also say that it is in our nature to be a poet, it is a part of our nature: a nature that we are born with but which later on strengthens and refines itself by adding certain other elements to itself as it sees fit. Because of this nature, we not only want to write poetry but we also want to read it.

Here, we can compare the poet at least partly to a *jīva*, a living being. The nature of any living being is innate, it is given to it as a living being. And the basic element of this nature is that the living being wants to live and wants to keep itself alive. In order to do that, more than anything else, it makes arrangements, such that it can eat and protect itself from other living beings and from natural disasters. In the same way, the human being, who also happens to be a poet by his (her) basic nature, keeps on writing poetry and keeps on reading it, besides doing other things, to keep himself alive as a poet.

Generally, we call this strong desire or drive to write poetry as talent. But talent is not the right word. It is simply a make-do word that we can keep using if we want to, but that word does not fully tell us why a person is a poet and wants to keep writing poetry.

You say that poetry is neither in verse nor in prose. For you these are forms of writing. If that is so, then where does poetry exist? How to recognise it?

I have said elsewhere that verse is often taken to be poetry and a poem which is not in verse but in prose is called a prose poem. And I had added that actually verse and prose are forms of writing and poetry can be written in both these forms. But still not every piece of verse contains poetry. Similarly, it is not proper to call a poem which is written in the form of prose as 'prose poetry' — it is just poetry.

Now, the question arises that if verse and prose are forms of writing and poetry can be written in both these forms, then where does poetry reside or exist? The answer is that poetry exists in words and sentences. It exists in the feelings and meanings that are inherent in the words chosen. And it exists in the way these words are combined in particular ways to form particular kinds of sentences and the feelings and meanings that are created out of these combinations of sentences.

If we go further, we can say that poetry also exists in the pauses and intervals which we introduce into verse or prose while composing poetry. And that it exists in the rhythm that is produced by a particular association of words, sentences, pauses and intervals.

It may be asked here that there are feelings and meanings even in the writings which we do not label or consider as poetry. So, what is it in poetry that is not there in non-poetic writing?

This question is connected with the question of what is poetry, a question which I have not been asked. Suffice it to say that poetry exists in special kinds of sets of words, sentences, pauses, intervals and the moods, meanings and rhythms that arise from them. These particular sets are different from the sets that do not constitute poetry. Secondly, these sets or combinations can be both in verse and in prose, and they can also be a mixture of these two forms of writing.

You have also written somewhere that for writing poetry,

technique is more important than content, thoughts and emotions. Can you explain this in some detail?

I said above that poetry consists in sets of words, sentences, pauses, intervals and the expressions, meanings and rhythms arising out of them. This means that feelings, thoughts, etc are inseparably connected with poetry, without them it is not possible to have poetry. But, at the same time, feelings, thoughts, etc can also be a part of the writing that does not contain poetry. In other words, there is something special which makes poetry what it is, which sets it apart from the writing that does not contain poetry.

But we will not consider what this 'special something' is. All we are concerned with here is that this 'something special,' this something extra, which makes poetry what it is, does not happen on its own; it does not form itself; it is made. And if it is made, if it is fabricated, it requires technique. And the poet should know this technique; rather, to be a good poet, she or he should master this technique, be its master.

To some extent, this technique is innate to the poet. But for the most part, he has to learn it. It is possible that a person is a poet by instinct, by nature, but without knowing this technique, he cannot write poetry; certainly, without knowing it he cannot write good poetry.

This technique comes from practising writing poetry over and over again. Secondly, it also comes from reading really good poets, whether they write in our own language or in some other language. It is this technique that tells us which sentence we should write complete to the end, which sentence to break, where to pause, where to keep the interval, where to use the dash, the hyphen, the bracket and so on. Similarly, with the help of this technique, we create rhythm in the poem, we can see whether the rhythm has not deteriorated in any part of the poem, and then with the help of this technique we correct it, improve it. This technique allows us to understand whether a word is heavier or lighter than it should be.

And if it is, we remove that word, replacing it with another word, even if doing so changes the meaning or sense of the sentence. Here we can see how we try to balance meaning and emotion on the one hand and rhythm on the other. This wouldn't be possible without knowledge of technique. Here we can also see how meaning or emotion is not paramount in poetry. Many times, we give up a meaning or a mood, change it to maintain the rhythm. What is

Rustam at 69, photographs in 2024

important is that ultimately a well-composed poem should emerge.

This shows that when we start writing poetry, we are in the grip of certain thoughts and feelings and we try to put them down on paper. But what often happens is that as we go along, we find that in order to retain poetry in what we are writing, we have to discard, to some extent change, the original thoughts and feelings that we had in mind. Instead of the words we wanted to use, some other words might have to be used. In this way we see that what ultimately becomes a poem is not exactly the same poem that we wanted to write. It has become to some extent, or at times to a great extent, a somewhat different, a somewhat new poem, of which we were not aware at the beginning. All this is not possible without knowing, understanding, mastering the technique of writing poetry. In the absence of the knowledge of technique, we may write a bad poem and may think that we have written a good poem.

It is because of the mastery of technique that an accomplished poet can bring some emotion into the poem without feeling it too deeply and yet may be able to write a high-quality poem. But it's not easy, only a great poet can do that.

It is often complained that the meaning of the poem is not clear or accessible. At times many readers directly ask the poet the meaning of a particular poem of his. Is it the responsibility of the poet to make clear or explain the meaning? What is meaning in the context of poetry?

There are different kinds of poetry. In some poems the meaning is clearer, in others less. There are different kinds of poets. Some poets want to make the meaning clear in their poetry, while some other poets want to maintain ambiguity so that their reader can see and absorb more than one meaning.

Meaning in poetry is ultimately what the reader understands or follows, not what the poet had or has in mind. It is therefore unnecessary to ask the poet what the meaning of his poem is. In fact, many times the poet himself does not know the exact meaning of his poem.

The poet should not be asked the meaning of his poem because after being written, the poem becomes independent of him, becomes free and creates its own existence. That becomes a third thing apart from the poet and the reader; it is no longer associated with the poet. So, the reader must connect directly with the poem and remove the poet from between himself and the poem.

But even then, if the reader does not understand the meaning of a poem, it means three things. The first is that the poet has hidden the meaning in the poem somewhere deep and that meaning has to be brought to the surface by reading the poem again and again. Secondly, the reader is not yet ready to read poetry and has to train himself as a reader by reading some good poets. Readers should understand that just as it takes practice to be a good poet, it also takes practice to be a competent reader.

There is a third thing. The meaning of many good poems is not understood because they are not meaning-oriented; rather they are rhythm-oriented. And when we read such poems, even if we do not fully understand their meaning, their rhythm is so strong and powerful that it grips us and we go on reading the poem, unable to stop. Therefore, it should also be said here that meaning is not everything in poetry, and that while reading a poem one should not be in search of meaning only. The poem should be taken in its totality.

What are your thoughts on what is called 'committed poetry'?

I believe that every poet should write what he can naturally write. So, if a poet is really concerned about social and political issues and feels that poetry can play a role in changing society or politics, or feels that the day-to-day concerns of the common person should find a place in poetry or can be articulated through poetry, then I think that poet should write such poems, provided they fulfil the standards of good poetry and are not just political rants. Poets from different languages of the world have written powerful poems involving political and social concerns, which have also been read a lot.

One problem with so-called committed poems is that they are often not good poems at all. They reveal ideas that are already known to people and that have already become prevalent through social sciences or ideology. The function of poetry is not to present ideological or political-sociological ideas. Social sciences can do the job better and it should be left to them. The work of poetry is not to do social science or to repeat its work. The genre of poetry and its nature are different from social sciences. And the so-called committed poets should try to understand this.

You write poems, you paint, you take photos. Do these three activities do the same thing, or do they do different things?

Apart from these three kinds of work, I also write philosophical and academic papers and articles, which are written in English. I think these are all different aspects of the same person. Importantly, they are not necessarily interconnected or cohere with one another. I have seen that many of the things that I cannot say in my philosophical writing emerge in poetry. And many times, the things said in the articles and poems contradict one another. The same can be said about me as a painter and photographer.

This means two things. Every genre has its own limitations. You can't say everything through the same genre. Secondly, there are different viewpoints within you that see things in their own ways. As I have also pointed out above, what these viewpoints see is not only different from what any other viewpoint sees, but it can also stand in opposition to it.

Your poems have been translated into many languages, and you have also translated many poets. What factors must be

taken into account in translation? Does the translated poem become the same as the original?

Every language has its own strengths. And it has its own limitations. These qualities or deficiencies affect not only the writing done in that language but also the translation done into it from other languages. This is why, for example, translations of Hindi poems into English often fail to do well.

There are basically two assumptions about the translation of poetry. One is that while translating a poem, we should stay as close as possible to the original poem. Second, when translating poetry, we can be somewhat experimental, translating more freely, even if the poem changes to some extent.

I believe in both of these concepts. I think the main thing is whether the poem is working and reading well in the language of translation or not. If the poetry in the original poem is breaking down, dissolving in the language of translation in an attempt to retain its meaning, expression and structure, we should not cling to the meaning, expression and structure of the original poem.

It needs to be said here that not only while writing a poem, but also while translating a poem, the most important thing is rhythm. If the rhythm is not taking shape or is breaking at one or more places in the translated poem, then at those places we have to change the translation. And in doing so, we may have to go a little further away from the meaning, the emotion or the structure in the original poem. Needless to say, like a poet, the ears of the translator of the poem should be attuned to music, because whether the rhythm is right or not is known only through the ears. I believe that the ability to sense the rhythm is innate. Just as everyone cannot be a good poet, not everyone can be a good translator.

In addition, whether the translation will turn out to be good or not also depends on the poem. Some poems are easily translated. It takes a lot of effort to translate some other poems. And there are poems which cannot at all be translated. We often skip these latter poems when translating, although sometimes they are the most important poems of a poet. A poem that is deeply rooted in the history, culture and language of its region is often difficult to translate. But that's not all. Often it is difficult to translate even poems with a deep philosophical vision. As soon as they are translated into another language, they lose their depth and become flat; they appear to be ordinary. Such poems have to be almost rewritten in the language of translation.

Finally, the translator should make an effort, as far as possible, to retain the pauses, colons, semi-colons, dashes, hyphens and spaces and intervals of the original poem. It goes without saying that not all of them can always be retained in translation exactly as they are in the original poem.

translated from Hindi by Rustam

Gurpreet (b 1968) is a well-known Panjabi poet. He has published five collections of poems, two books in prose and two books for children. He has also compiled and edited one book and translated four titles. He has received the following awards for poetry: Prof Mohan Singh Kavita Puraskar; Shah Chaman Yadgari Puraskar; Kanwar Chauhan Kavita Puraskar; and Prof Joga Singh Yadgari Puraskar. He is currently a research officer in the Language Department, Government of Panjab.

by **Rustam**

Poetry in Hindi

Agyanata Se Agyanata Tak (self-published), 1981.
Rustam Ki Kavitaen, Vani Prakashan, New Delhi, 2003.
Teji Aur Rustam Ki Kavitaen, HarperCollins India, Noida, 2009.
(This book contains selected poems by Rustam and Teji Grover).
Meri Atma Kanpti Hai, Surya Prakashan Mandir, Bikaner, 2015.
Ped Neela Tha Aur Anya Kavitayen, Eklavya, Bhopal, 2016.
This collection has poems for teenagers.
Na To Main Kuchh Keh Raha Tha, Surya Prakashan Mandir, Bikaner, 2020.
Jo Hai Aur Jaisa Hai, Surya Prakashan Mandir, Bikaner, 2021.
Sooni Sadkon Par Jab Main Vahan Ghoom Raha Tha, Surya Prakashan Mandir, Bikaner, 2021.
Main Prithvi Se Bichhud Gyaa Tha, Sambhavna Prakashan, Hapur, 2024.
Kyonki Main Phool Ki Chhaya Mein Tha, Surya Prakashan Mandir, Bikaner, 2024.
(This book is a new edition of *Rustam Ki Kavitaen*, Vani Prakashan, 2003.)
Aur Kash Ki Main Aik Neeli Shila Hota: Chuni Hui Kavitaen: 1985-2020, Surya Prakashan Mandir, Bikaner, 2021.
(This book has selected poems of Rustam from 1985 to 2020).
Bahar Sab Shaant Hai, Aadhar Prakashan, Panchkula, 1991.
(Some of Rustam's poems figures in this collection of poems by fourteen Hindi poets. This collection was edited by Desh Nirmohi.)
Ek Khushboo Vahan Phaili Thee, Surya Prakashan Mandir, Bikaner, 2026.

Translations of Rustam's Poetry

English:

Indian Literature, New Delhi: 158 (Nov-Dec, 1993: Tr by Teji Grover).
International Quarterly, Tallahassee, USA: Vol. 3, No. 2: (1998: Tr by Teji Grover).
Indian Literature, New Delhi: 251 (May-June, 2009: Tr by Rustam and Teji Grover).
Aufgabe13, Berkeley, USA (2014: Tr by Rustam and Teji Grover).
Dialog, Chandigarh: No. 27 (Spring 2015: Tr by Teji Grover).

Swedish:

Lyrikvannen, Stockholm: No. 1/06 (2006: Tr by Agneta Pleijel).
Lyrikvannen, Stockholm: No. 5 (2015: Tr by Agneta Pleijel).

Estonian:

https://www.sirp.ee/tuhandevarvine-kivi/ (9.1.2015: Tr by Doris Kareva).
Looming, Tallinn: No 11 (2023: Tr by Doris Kareva).

Panjabi:

Filhal, Mohali: No. 29 (2020: Tr by Bipanpreet)
Pre-Poetic, Panjab: No 1 (January 2021: Tr by Ambrish)

In addition to the above, Rustam's poems have been translated into Norwegian, French, Spanish, Telugu, Marathi and Malayalam.

Readings

Apart from giving numerous readings of his poems in India, Rustam has read his poems in other countries as well. For example, in 2008, he read his poems in the international poetry festival organised by the Baltic Centre for Writers and Translators, Visby, Sweden. The Swedish translations of his poems were read out by Birgitta Wallin, editor of the Swedish literary and cultural magazine *Karavan*. In the same year, he was invited to read his poems at the poetry festival celebrating the birth centenary of the famous Norwegian poet Olav Hauge at the village Ulvik in north-western Norway where Hauge had lived all his life. In 2011, he read his poems during the India Festival at Trondheim, Norway. The Norwegian translations of his poems were read out by Ingrid Storholmen, Norwegian poet and novelist. Similarly, in 2014 he was invited to read his poems at the Writers House in Tallinn, Estonia, where the Estonian translations of his poems were read out by the well-known Estonian poet Doris Kareva.

Translations into Hindi by Rustam (under the name Rustam Singh)

(With Teji Grover) *Hedda Gabler* by Henrik Ibsen, Vani Prakashan, New Delhi, 2006.
(With Teji Grover) *Master Builder* by Henrik Ibsen, Vani Prakashan, New Delhi, 2006.
Saat Havayen, Vani Prakashan, New Delhi, 2008.
A selection of poems by the famous Norwegian poet Olav Hauge.
Shabd Ke Peechhe Chhaya Hai, Vani Prakashan, New Delhi, 2014.
A selection of poems by the Norwegian poet and novelist Lars Amund Vaage.
Bindu, Eklavya, Bhopal, 2014. Translation of *Raza's Bindu* by Ritu Khoda and Vanita Pai. It's a book for children on the well-known Indian painter Syed Haider Raza.
(With Teji Grover) *Aag Jo Jalati Nahin*, Rajkamal Prakashan, New Delhi, 2021.
A selection of poems by the well-known Estonian poet Doris Kareva.
Jab Main Ghar Pahuncha To Ghoda Ja Chuka Tha, Eklavya, Bhopal, 2021.
A story book for children by Norwegian poet and writer Hans Sande.
Aa Jao Ab Raat, Eklavya, Bhopal, 2021.
A story book for children by Norwegian poet and writer Hans Sande.
Saat Panjabi Kavi, Surya Prakashan Mandir, Bikaner, 2023.
A selection of poems of seven Panjabi poets.

Anthology

Kuchh Alag Swar: Atharah Samkaleen Hindi Kavi, Surya Prakashan Mandir, Bikaner, 2025. This is an anthology of the poems of eighteen contemporary Hindi poets.

Books in English (under the name Rustam Singh)

A Story of Political Ideas for Young Readers, Volume 1: Socrates, Plato, Aristotle, Machiavelli, Eklavya, Bhopal, 2010.
'Weeping' and Other Essays on Being and Writing, Pratilipi Books, Jaipur, 2011.
Violence and Marxism: Marx to Mao, Aakar Books, New Delhi, 2015.
Literature, Philosophy, Political Theory: Selected Essays, Aakar Books, New Delhi, 2022.

Papers and Essays in English (under the name Rustam Singh)

"Status of Violence in Marx's Theory of Revolution," *Economic and Political Weekly*, Vol. XXIV, No. 4 (January 28, 1989).
"Restoring Revolutionary Theory: Towards an Understanding of Lenin's The State and Revolution," *Economic and Political Weekly*, Vol. XXIV, No. 43 (October 28, 1989).
"Violence in the Leninist Revolution," *Economic and Political Weekly*, Vol. XXV, No. 52 (December 29, 1990).
"Cohen's Second Coming: Pitfalls of Analytical Interpretation of Marx," *Punjab Journal of Politics*, Vol. XVII, No. 1 (June 1993).
"Man, Political Man, Political Theory," *Economic and Political Weekly*, Vol. XXIX, No. 31 (July 30, 1994).
"Reflections on a Form," *Seminar*, 440 (April 1996).
"Ontology of Wage Labour," *Seminar*, 452 (April 1997).
"Feeling Politics: Reinstating the Subjective Self," *Economic and Political Weekly*, Vol. XXXII, No. 33-34 (August 16–23, 1997).
"Dialogicality and Being: A Fragment," *Studies in Humanities and Social Sciences*, Vol. V, No. 1 (Summer 1998), IIAS, Shimla.
"'Weeping': For Udayan Vajpeyi," *Indian Literature*, No. 186 (July–August 1998).
"Gift, Passivity, Neuter," in Franson Manjali (ed), *Poststructuralism and Cultural Theory: The Linguistic Turn and Beyond*, Allied Publishers, New Delhi, 2006.
"Useless Thought: Notes on Friedrich Nietzsche," in Franson Manjali (ed), *Nietzsche: Philologist, Philosopher and Cultural Critic*, Allied Publishers, New Delhi, 2006.
"Self and Time," *Pratilipi*, April 2008.
"Death and the Self," *Pratilipi*, June 2008.
"To be Regardful of the Earth", *Pratilipi*, August 2008.
"To be Fortunate," *Pratilipi*, June 2010.
"Beginning an Essay," *Pratilipi*, November 2010.
"Simulating: The Heart Breaking," *Comparative and Continental Philosophy*, Vol. 4, No. 2 (2012).
"Roots of Violence: Jīva, Life and Other Things," in Saitya Brata Das and Soumyabrata Choudhury (eds), *The Weight of Violence: Religion, Language,*

Politics, Oxford University Press, New Delhi, 2015.
"Not This, Not That: Maurice Blanchot and Poststructuralism," *Comparative and Continental Philosophy*, Vol. 8, No. 1 (2016).
"Not This, Not That: Maurice Blanchot and Poststructuralism," in Franson Manjali and Marc Crepon (eds), *Philosophy, Language and the Political: Poststructuralism in Perspective*, Aakar Books, New Delhi, 2018.
"Visual Objects: Types, Forms and Status," *New Horizons: A Multidisciplinary Research Journal*, Vol. XV (August 2018).
"Humans, the Earth and Nonhuman Animals: Language, Politics, Ethics," in Saitya Brata Das (ed), *Language and Culture: Essays in Honour of Franson Manjali*, Aakar Books, Delhi, 2024.

Rustam and Teji Grover reading poetry in Norway, 2008

Born in Panjab in, 1955, TEJI GROVER is a Hindi poet, fiction writer, translator and painter. She is an important voice in Hindi poetry in the generations born after 1950. She has published several collections of poetry, a novel, a collection of short stories, a collection of essays and a book of auto-fiction. Her poetry, fiction and essays have been translated into many Indian and foreign languages and have been widely published in journals across the world. Her novel *Neela* has been published in Polish and English translations, and her collected fiction was published in English translation in 2020. A volume of her selected poetry was published in 2019 in Swedish translation. She has also been widely anthologised as a poet. As a painter, she has exhibited her works in several galleries both home and abroad. She has developed her own repertoire of ecological colours extracted from natural substances, and shares her knowledge widely for environmental reasons. Teji Grover has introduced some of the most significant modern Scandinavian writers and poets to the Hindi reader, such as Knut Hamsun, Tarjei Vesaas, Jon Fosse, Kjell Askildsen, Gunnar Björling, Hans Herbjørnsrud, Edith Södergran, Tomas Tranströmer, Lars Lundkvist, and Ann Jäderlund, among many others, as also the French writer Marguerite Duras, the Latvian writer Nora Ikstena and the Estonian poet Doris Kareva. She has received the following awards and fellowships: Bharat Bhushan Agrawal Award for poetry (1989); Writer-in-Residence/Director, Premchand Srijanpeeth, Ujjain (1995-1997); Senior Fellowship (Literature), Department of Culture, Ministry of Human Resource Development, Government of India, New Delhi (1995-1997); Sayed Haider Raza (SH Raza) Award for poetry (2003); Fellowship at the Institute of Advanced Study, Nantes, France (2016-2017); and Vani Foundation Distinguished Translator Award (2019). She was created Dame by the King and the Queen of Sweden (2019), receiving The Royal Order of the Polar Star, Member 1st Class, for promoting literary and cultural relations between India and Sweden.

tejigrover@yahoo.co.in

Red River Poetry in Translation Series

The Wild Weed: Selected Poems by Paul Kaur
translated from the Punjabi by Arvinder Kaur

I'm Your Poet: Selected Poems by Nilim Kumar
translated from the Assamese by Dibyajyoti Sarma

The Smell of Man: Selected Poems by Thangjam Ibopishak
translated from the Manipuri by Robin S Ngangom

Evening with a Sufi by Afsar Mohammad
translated from the Telugu by Afsar Mohammad & Shamala Gallagher

i, Salma: Selected Poems by Salma
translated from the Telugu by K Srilata and Shobhana Kumar
conceptualised and curated by Chandana Dutta

July: North by Andréane Frenette-Vallières
translated from the French by Peter Schulman

Bless Us All by Veera Rathod
translated from the Marathi by LS Deshpande

In the Light of Shiva by HS Shivaprakash
translated from the Kannada by HS Shivaprakash and others
edited by Kamalakar Bhat

Red River Poetry in Translation Series

Scratching the Silence by Prafull Shiledar
translated from the Marathi by Santosh Bhoomkar,
Vishnu Khare, Maya Pandit & Dilip Chavan

Earth Song: Selected Poems by Kanji Patel
translated from the Gujarati by Dileep Jhaveri

Perennial: The Red River Book of 21st Century Hindi Poetry
selected & edited by Sourav Roy & Tuhin Bhowal

Alone in the Night River by Mukunda Ramarao
translated from the Telugu by M Sridhar & Alladi Uma

Open Your Door, Library by Trishna Basak
translated from the Bengali by Nabanita Sengupta

Voices from the Bodo Heartlands: Twelve Women Poets in Translation
edited by Zothanchhingi Khiangte & Manab Medhi

Five Modern Bengali Poets
selected & edited by Nirmal Kanti Bhattacharjee